Twelve Short Pieces for Piano

# Lazy Days

Brian Chapple

Exclusive distributors:
**Music Sales Limited**
Newmarket Road, Bury St. Edmunds, Suffolk IP33 3YB.

UK ISBN 0.7119.2293.4
Order No. CH55983

Cover designed by Helen Senior

**Chester Music Limited**
A division of Music Sales Limited

# Hopscotch

CH 55983

# March

# Sleigh Ride

# Snake Charmer

# Petite Valse

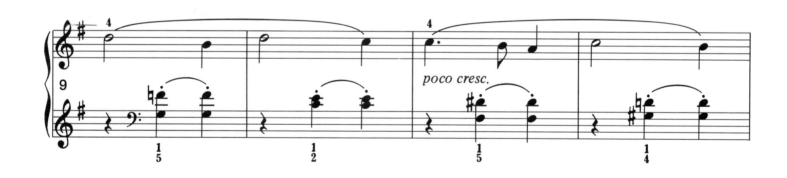

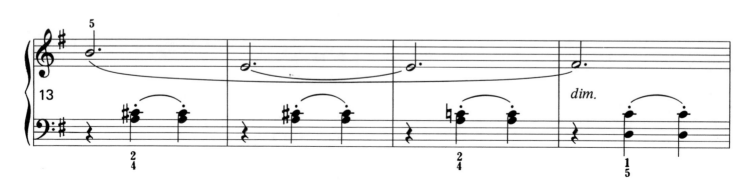

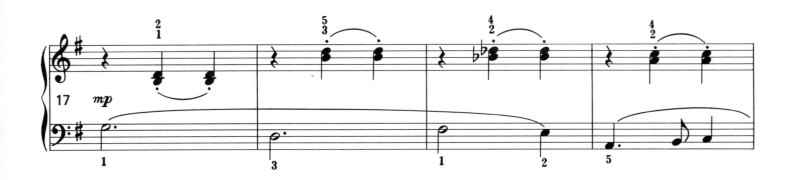

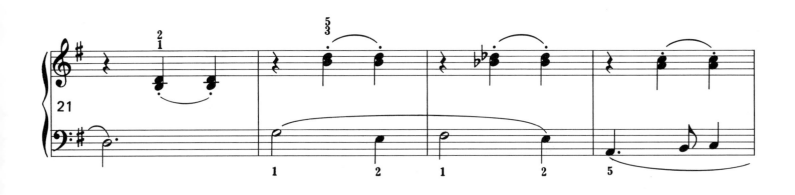

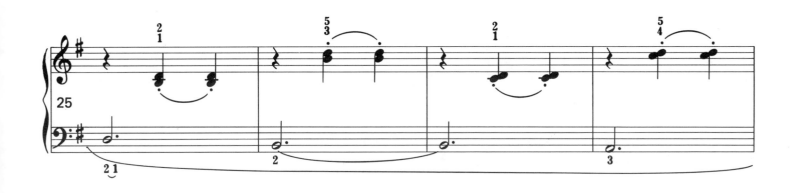

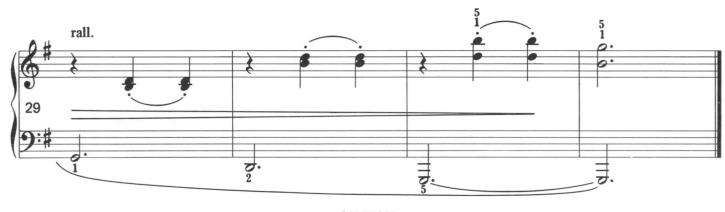

# Wrong Number

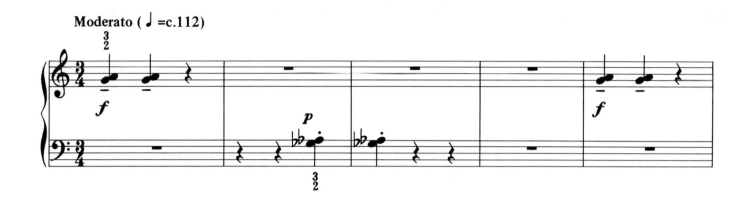

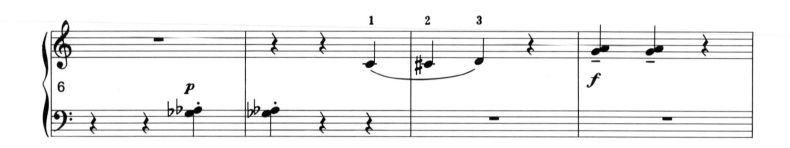

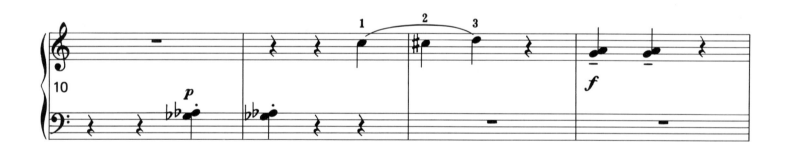

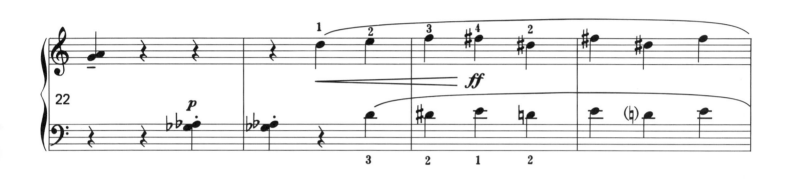

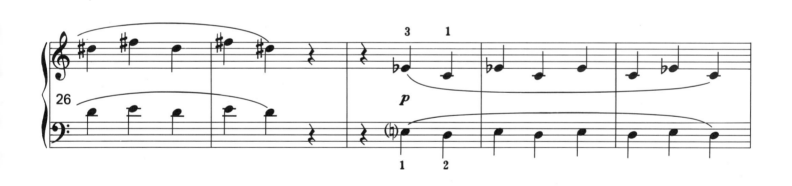

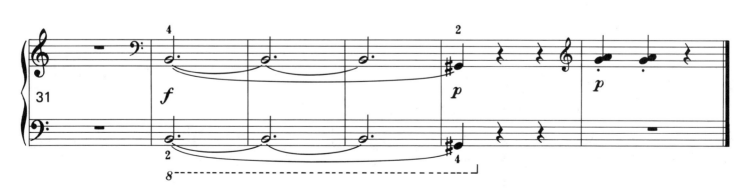

# Waltz Variations

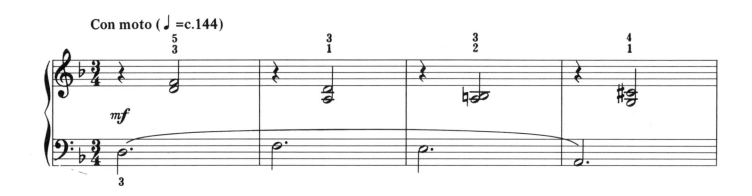

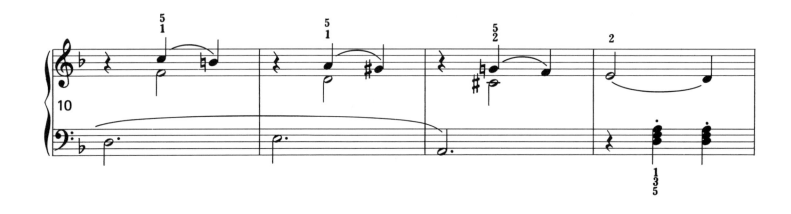

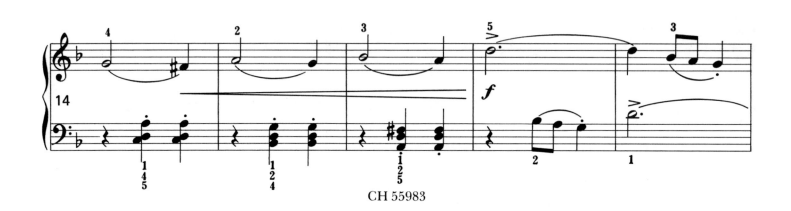

# The Snow Melts

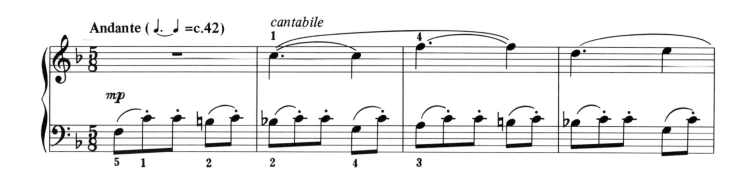

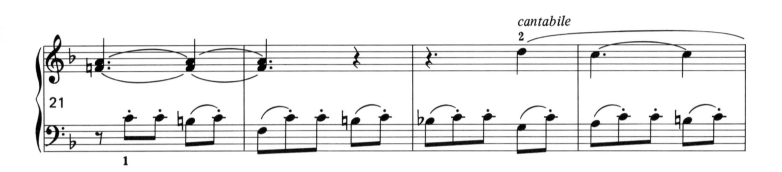

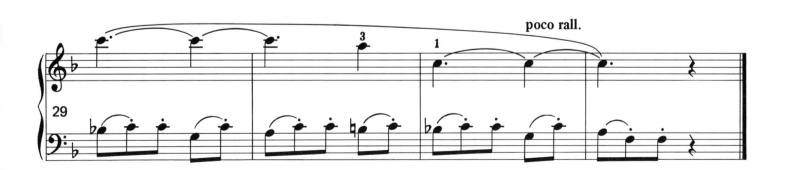

# Clocks

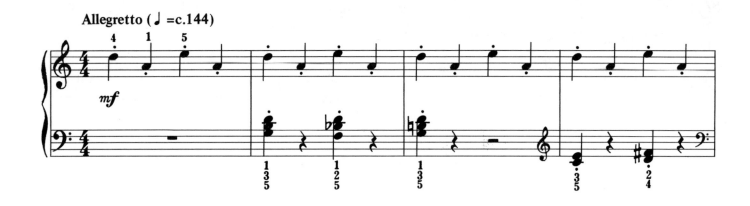

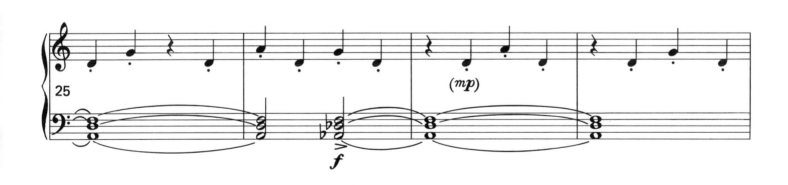

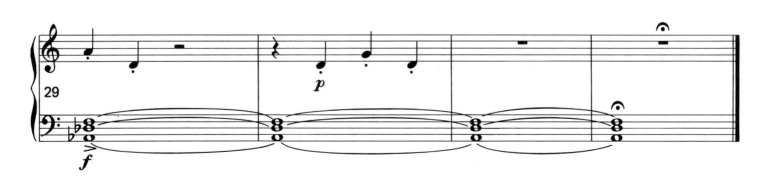

# Lazy Days

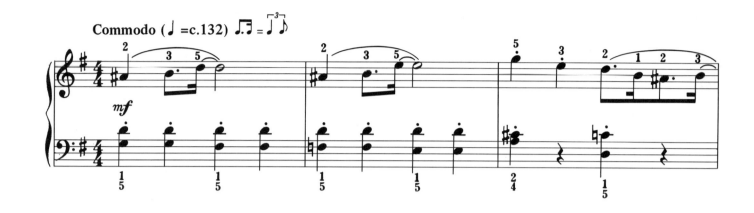

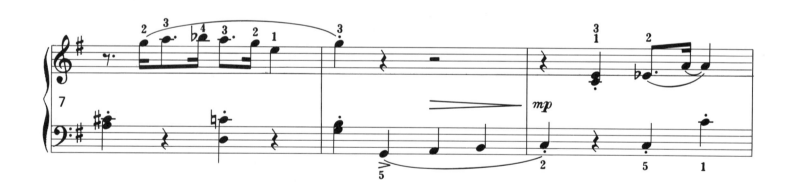

# Blues

# Tango